THE BLACKSMITH

KICKSTART

LOS ANGELES · CALIFORNIA

THE BLACKSMITH

CREATED & WRITTEN BY
MALIK EVANS &
RICHARD SPARKMAN

ART & COVER BY **ALBERTO MURIEL**

COLORS BY **MARC RUEDA**

LETTERS & DESIGN BY **BILL TORTOLINI**

PRODUCED BY **KICKSTART COMICS INC.**

For Kickstart Comics Inc:
Samantha Shear, Managing Editor
Special Thanks to Jeremy Stein

Address correspondence to: Kickstart Comics Inc.
480 Washington Ave., North Suite 201, Ketchum, ID. 83340

THERE ARE A HUNDRED AND NINETY-FIVE COUNTRIES IN THE WORLD.

BUT ONLY ONE BEARS THE CROWN IN WARFARE.

AMERICA ALWAYS HAS ONE EYE OPEN AND A FINGER ON THE TRIGGER.

I WANT YOU DEAD

BLACKSMITH, IF I HADN'T SEEN YOUR WORK I WOULD THINK YOU WERE SCREWING WITH ME.

YOU'LL HAVE IT AT THE NEXT DROP.

GOOD. WHAT'S NEW WITH THE ARMAGEDDON RIFLE? ANY MORE PROGRESS?

IT NEEDS WORK, BUT I'M NOT SURE I'M EVER GOING TO FINISH IT.

THEY WON'T STOP ASKING ABOUT IT. THEY'RE WILLING TO PAY TOP DOLLAR.

SOME WEAPONS SHOULD NEVER BE BUILT, NO MATTER THE PRICE TAG.

YOU GROWING A CONSCIENCE ON ME BLACKSMITH? YOU COULD MAKE A FORTUNE.

WHAT GOOD IS A FORTUNE IF YOU'RE NOT HERE TO SPEND IT? I BUILD WEAPONS THAT KEEP US SAFE.

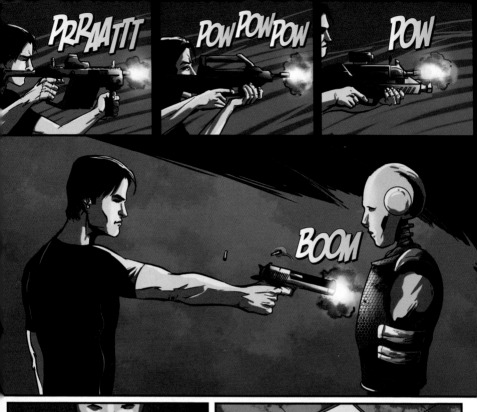

WHAT TYPE OF MUSIC SHOULD WE RIDE TO TODAY, TIGER? ROCK? JAZZ? COUNTRY? OR MY FAVORITE, COMPLETE SILENCE?

WROOOMM

SECURITY
SYSTEM ON

WIPE YOUR
FEET.

SO TIGER
WHAT DO YOU
WANT FOR
DINNER?

LOOKS
LIKE SPAGHETTI
AGAIN.

SELECT:
spaghetti
456 Cal.

I CAN'T EXPLAIN NOW, BUT CAN YOU TAKE MY DOG FOR AWHILE?

YOUR DOG? ARE YOU IN SOME KIND OF TROUBLE?

IF I LIVE THROUGH IT, I'LL COME BACK AND TELL YOU SOMEDAY. HIS NAME IS TIGER. HE'LL EAT ANYTHING.

WE HAVE A SUSPECT ON FOOT. WHITE MALE. LATE TWENTIES, EARLY THIRTIES, 5'10. NEAR WASHINGTON STREET. OVER.

STOP RIGHT THERE!

SOMEWHERE IN NEW JERSEY.

HE GOT AWAY. THE ONLY THING HE LEFT WAS A FEW SHAKEN UP COPS.

FOR A MAN WHO MAKES WEAPONS, HE SURE MAKES A POINT OF NOT HURTING ANYONE.

IT LOOKS LIKE OUR GUY KNOWS HOW TO IMPROVISE.

HE'S WORTH BILLIONS TO OUR NATIONAL SECURITY.

BUT NOW THAT HE'S ON THE RUN, WHO KNOWS WHO HE'LL OFFER HIS SERVICES TO. THE MORE TIME HE HAS, THE MORE DANGEROUS HE WILL BECOME.

THE MORE HE SCREWS WITH US, THE MORE PISSED MY TEAM BECOMES.

COME ON GUYS, WE'RE DONE HERE. WE HAVE WORK TO DO.

WHO ARE YOU?

SOMEBODY THAT USED TO TRUST YOU.

WAIT A MINUTE. BLACKSMITH? IS IT REALLY YOU? I IMAGINED YOU WOULD BE A LOT BIGGER -- AND TALLER.

IS THIS GUN BIG ENOUGH FOR YOU? I WANT TO KNOW HOW SOME MANIACS GOT A HOLD OF MY DESIGNS.

I DON'T KNOW WHAT YOU'RE TALKING ABOUT!

DIDN'T CATCH THE TEN O'CLOCK NEWS? SOMEONE JUST BLASTED A SENATOR WITH A WEAPON I BUILT AND THE FEDS CAME KNOCKING AT MY DOOR WITH ASSAULT RIFLES AND FORTY FIVES!

I SELL YOUR WEAPONS TO THE U.S. GOVERNMENT. THAT'S IT.

YOU THINK I'D BE LIVING IN A DUMP LIKE THIS IF I WERE SELLING YOUR WEAPONS TO THE HIGHEST BIDDER?

WELL, SOMEONE SET ME UP. AND YOU'RE THE ONLY ONE I DEAL WITH.

YOU'RE POINTING THE FINGER AND THE GUN AT THE WRONG PERSON. C'MON KID, PUT THE GUN DOWN.

LISTEN, I'M JUST THE MIDDLEMAN. I MAKE A GOOD LIVING WORKING VERY LITTLE HOURS, DOUBLE CROSSING THE U.S. GOVERNMENT IS OUT OF MY PAY GRADE.

THINK FOR A MINUTE. LET'S ASSUME ONLY THE US GOVERNMENT HAS YOUR DESIGNS AND YOU WERE SET UP. IS THERE ANOTHER BLACKSMITH CAPABLE OF REPLICATING YOUR WORK?

THERE'S ONLY ONE OTHER PERSON. BULLET.

BULLET? WHO'S BULLET?

HE'S MOSTLY A DEMOLITION EXPERT, AN OLD FRIEND OF MY FATHER'S. FIGURED HE COULD MAKE MORE MONEY SELLING HIS CREATIONS ON THE BLACK MARKET. TOTAL BASTARD BUT HE CAN REVERSE ENGINEER ALMOST ANYTHING.

WHERE ARE YOU GOING?

TO FIND A WORM IN THE BIG APPLE.

AAAAHHH!

STAY DOWN!

I'LL LIVE. THEY'RE HERE FOR YOU KID. I'LL COVER YOU. HEAD OUT THE BACK, THERE'S AN ALLEY.

NO!

SOMEONE HAS TO HOLD THEM OFF!

I OWE YOU ONE.

DON'T WORRY, I CAN TAKE CARE OF MYSELF! NOW, GO!

Emergency
Brake

AAARRRGHH!

I DON'T WANT TO HURT YOU. JUST TELL ME WHY!

LOOK I NEED TO KNOW WHAT YOU KNOW. I KNOW YOU HEARD ABOUT THE MURDER OF THE SENATOR. YOU SAW THE WEAPON THEY USED. YOU ARE THE ONLY PERSON WHO COULD RECREATE THAT. I WANT TO KNOW WHY.

I'M SORRY ALEX. I DIDN'T KNOW IT WAS YOU. I SHOULD HAVE. I TRAINED YOU JUST AS MUCH AS YOUR FATHER.

LATER, WASHINGTON D.C., THE PENTAGON.

EVERYTHING IS CLASSIFIED, BUT IT LOOKS LIKE THEY WERE COVERT OPS TURNED WAR CRIMINALS. REALLY BAD GUYS.

WHAT'D WE FIND OUT ABOUT THIS WOLFPACK?

WAIT, THEY'RE DEAD?

WELL, THEY WERE BEING HELD IN A FEDERAL PENITENTIARY AWAITING TRIAL, BUT WHILE THEY WERE BEING TRANSFERRED, THE BUS BLEW UP. NEVER DID FIND THE BODIES...

I THINK THEY CAN STOP LOOKING. AND DAN, KEEP THIS BETWEEN US.

I'M ON MY WAY.

DOES MY OFFICE LOOK DIRTY TO YOU?

SORRY SIR.

WAIT!

DON'T FORGET THE TRASH.

I CAN STILL MAKE THAT HAPPEN. LET'S FINISH WHAT WE PLANNED.

THE PLAN WAS TO FIND HIS WEAPONS.

IT STILL IS, BUT HE'S GOT A LOT MORE PLANS IN HIS HEAD.

WELL THEN WE NEED HIM WITHIN 24 HOURS, I'VE GOT PEOPLE WAITING. AND THEY ARE NOT PATIENT.

WE HAVE TO GET TO HIM BEFORE THE CIA AND THIS HARD ASS GREY DOES. IF THEY CATCH HIM FIRST ALL THIS WAS FOR NOTHING.

WHAT'S GOING ON!?

HELLO MISS GREY. DO NOT BE ALARMED, I'LL TAKE THE WHEEL FOR NOW.

BLACKSMITH!? STOP THE CAR NOW!

NOT UNTIL AFTER YOU WATCH THE MOVIE I MADE FOR YOU.

HOW ARE YOU DOING THIS?!

WATCH YOUR SCREEN, I'LL DRIVE.

THE MAN IN THIS VIDEO IS THE SAME MAN WHO SHOT BULLET.

BLACKSMITH! WATCH THE TRUCK!

KEEP YOUR EYES ON THE SCREEN AND I'LL KEEP MY EYES ON THE ROAD.

STOP THE CAR! I'M WATCHING!

WE HAVE TO GET TO HIM BEFORE THE CIA AND THIS HARD ASS GREY DOES. IF THEY CATCH HIM ALL THIS WAS FOR NOTHING.

THIS IS INSANE, IT WAS REYNOLDS ALL ALONG?

I TOLD YOU I WAS INNOCENT.

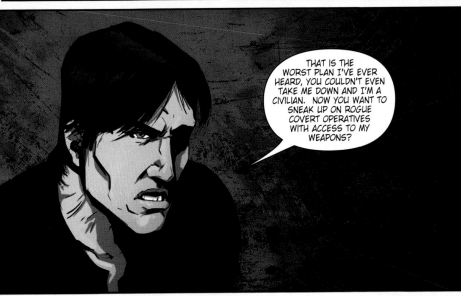

BACK AT CIA HEADQUARTERS.

REYNOLDS, GRAB YOUR GUN, IT'S SHOW TIME! WE FOUND THE BLACKSMITH!

WHERE IS HE?

PIGEON FORGE CABINS. RIGHT HERE IN D.C.

HE CHECKED IN LAST NIGHT. CABIN 24.

I'LL CALL POLICE UNITS IN THE AREA, TELL THEM IT'S A DRUG BUST.

NO. NO BACKUP, JUST LIKE THE GENERAL SAID. WE CAN HANDLE THIS DISCREETLY.

CALL YOUR TEAM WHEN WE ARRIVE. I'LL MEET YOU AT THE CAR.

ROMAN IS AT PIGEON FORGE CABINS. CABIN 24.

THE CIA IS ON THE WAY, SO MOVE QUICKLY. AND BRING HIM TO ME ALIVE.

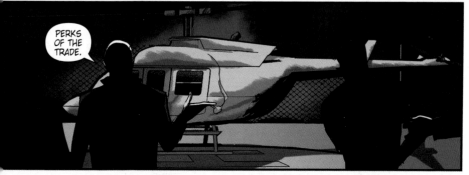

SORRY, BLACKSMITH, LOVE TO STAY AND CHAT, BUT WE'RE EXPECTING COMPANY. YOU TWO TAKE HIM BELOW.

YES SIR.

AND WATCH HIM, HE'S SLIPPERY.

YESSIR!

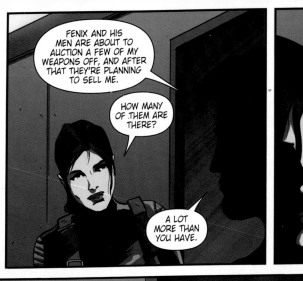

WHAT IS THAT?

HOMEMADE TEAR GAS.

WEEKS LATER.

WASHINGTON D.C.

PENTAGON

THAT'S ONE HELL OF A STORY MISS GREY.

AS FOR REYNOLDS, HE WAS ALWAY A BAD SEED IN THIS AGENCY.

SO NOW THAT YOU KNOW ABOUT OUR PROGRAM, I'VE GOT ANOTHER JOB FOR YOU. SEEMS WE'VE GOT A ROGUE BLACKSMITH IN MIAMI, I THINK THIS ONE MIGHT ACTUALLY BE GUILTY.

I'LL GET RIGHT ON IT.

AND GREY, IF YOU HEAR FROM MALLOY, TELL HIM WE COULD USE HIM ON THIS.

DIVINE WIND

WRITTEN BY JEFF Y. AMANO

HAKATA BAY, JAPAN.

"The other day, a boy cut off the head of a snake. His parents cried out to me, wanting to know if their son committed a karmic transgression."

"I told them to reward their son with a sweet bean cake."

"Had the snake entered my temple, it would be well-cared for. Had the snake remained in the forest, he would enjoy the bounty of the wild. But it ventured into the boy's home and paid the price of trespass."

"That is the Way of things."

"Across the Sea of Japan..."

"... a swarm of serpents have slithered through China, knowing no boundaries,..."

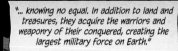

"... knowing no equal. In addition to land and treasures, they acquire the warriors and weaponry of their conquered, creating the largest military force on Earth."

"But it was not enough for Kublai Khan, Lord of the Mongols."

I'M NOT ASKING YOU TO BE MY MOM, RIGGS, I JUST NEED HELP REMEMBERING THINGS LIKE "BUY JUICE WHEN WE RUN OUT" AND OH, "IT'S MY DAUGHTER'S BIRTHDAY."

THAT ELEPHANT GHOUL? HE WAS DIGGING IN THE YARD BURYING BIGFOOT BONES!

GUESS YOU SHOULDN'T HAVE PISSED OFF SAM.

AND? THAT'S WHAT SAM DOES. YOU GONNA CITE BIGFOOT FOR LEAVING TRACKS? NOW PUT THIS ON. JUST A ROUTINE CHECK OF YOUR EXTRA SENSORIES.

COULD I GET A PEDICURE WITH THIS MAGAZINE?

YOU'RE LUCKY TO GET A MAGAZINE.

WHAT ARE YOU WEARING, HERMACHI?

IT'S VERSACE. HIMACHI'S A FISH.

NICE. SEBASTIAN MUST PAY YOU WELL.

THERE!

WHAT THE -- I DIDN'T SEE *THAT* LAST NIGHT...

BECAUSE HE'S EMITTING ON A FIFTY HERTZ CYCLE. YOUR EXTRA SENSORY DIDN'T PICK UP ON IT.

I'M LOSING MY TOUCH. DON'T TELL SEBASTIAN.

IT'S OK. I PLANTED HIM THERE.

YOU'RE TESTING ME?

SEBASTIAN ORDERED IT. HEY, DON'T WORRY, IT'S NOT LIKE YOU HAVE RABIES OR ANYTHING.

IT'S OUR ANNIVERSARY?

DON'T BE LATE FOR OUR ANNIVERSARY DINNER.

FOURTEENTH. HAVE FUN.

HOW ABOUT THANKS RIGGS?

Check out these great comics

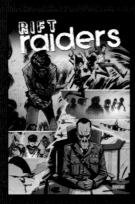

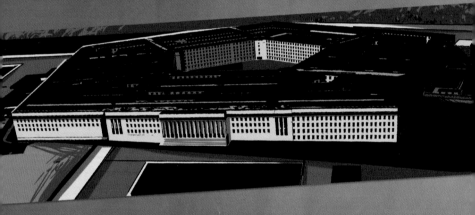

THE BLACKSMITH

KICKSTART
LOS ANGELES · CALIFORNIA